# Lizzie
## McGUIRE

Oh
My ^ Guide to:
# SCHOOL

# MORE OF MY BOOKS TO CHECK OUT!

**WHEN MOMS ATTACK!**

**TOTALLY CRUSHED!**

**LIZZIE GOES WILD**

**THE RISE AND FALL OF THE KATE EMPIRE**

**PICTURE THIS**

**NEW KID IN SCHOOL**

**BROKEN HEARTS**

**JUST LIKE LIZZIE**

**MY QUIZ BOOK**
More than 20 quizzes about boys, school,
friends – and me!

**DON'T EVEN GO THERE!**
A little book of Lizzie-isms

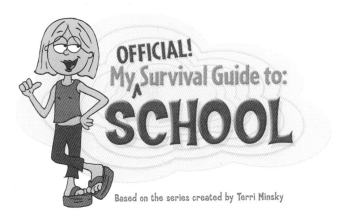

OFFICIAL!
My Survival Guide to:
SCHOOL

Based on the series created by Terri Minsky

EGMONT

First published in Great Britain 2004
by Egmont Books Limited
239 Kensington High Street, London W8 6SA

Written by Christien Haywood
Published by arrangement with Disney Press,
114 Fifth Avenue, New York, New York 10011-5690

Copyright © 2004 Disney Enterprises, Inc.

ISBN 1 4052 1137 7
1 3 5 7 9 10 8 6 4 2

A CIP catalogue record for this title is available
from the British Library

Printed and bound in the UK

# Contents

# Why YOU Need ME

HI THERE! I'm Lizzie – but you already knew *that*, right?
How was school today – pretty rough? Forget to hand in
your homework? Hit in the face by three dodgeballs?
*Totally* ignored by your crush boy?

Let's face it, school is a nightmare – unless you've got the
inside track. I learned *that* the hard way.

Lizzie: nil
Total humiliation:
fifty million

Trust me on this, you need a guide to help you get to the end of the week – and that's where I can help!

Just call me
*Lizzie McGuire:
Survivor Supreme!*

So check out my handy hints for surviving school – we girls have to stick together! Ever wondered how to tell if he's *really* crushing on you? Or how to survive science? How to avoid field trips? What to say to Mathletes? And how to avoid dork status? OK, so maybe I'm still working on that, but read on and let ol' Lizzie take the strain.

First off, it's essential to know who's got your back…and who's gossiping *behind* your back. Take a look at my list, and think about who your besties are…

# The Girls

**Name:** Miranda Sanchez

**A.K.A.:** My bestie

**Biog:** She's clever, she's cool, and I don't think I've *ever* seen her wear the same outfit twice. *Every* girl should have a Miranda!

**Most likely to say:** 'I agree – Ethan *is* edible!'

**Least likely to say:** 'Wow, Gordo! Tell me *more* about African Throat Singing!'

**Weak spots:** Ryan in theatre class (he's like Miranda *kryptonite*). Eating too much flan. And sometimes being just a teeeensy bit too sure of herself.

**Best moment:** Taking the rap for me when I emailed the whole school that Kate was only popular because she stuffed her … oh, you've already *heard* about that.

Gotta make up for that acting ability somehow…

**Worst moment:** Going to the Pool Party without me … But it turned out OK.

**Could surprise you by:** Learning to play the violin, and having a pretty cool singing voice.

**Survival strategy:** Cherish her! A good friend is hard to find. She's as indispensable as air, water and *lip balm*.

**Name:** Kate Sanders

**A.K.A.:** The Queen of Mean

**Biog:** Kate and me used to be best buds, but then something came between us…actually *two* things. One training bra later she's *Ms Congeniality* and I'm as popular as Tudgeman. Now she's got a big head, big hair, big popularity ratings and a big *head*. I did mention that she's got a big *head*, right?

Like, just the once!

**Most likely to say:** 'Hey, nice haircut Lizzie! Where did you get it – your mom do it for you?'

**Least likely to say:** 'I'm holding out for *Gordo* to ask me on a date.'

**Weak spots:** Ethan Kraft. Emails about bra stuffing (oops!).

**Best moment:** Remembering we used to be friends when we had a class assignment on Latvian cooking. Who would have thought an *Alexander Torte* could bring us together?

**Worst moment:** Hmm, putting those posters up of Miranda as a dog? Or maybe when her cheerleading squad made up a song about me? Or at Halloween when she made me wear a totally lame clown outfit? Or …

**Could surprise you by:** Forgetting she's the Prom Queen and being nice… for one *millisecond*!

**Survival strategy:** Ignore her. Popularity isn't everything …*is it*?

**Name:** Lizzie McGuire

**A.K.A.:** Lizz*eee*

**Biog:** As a great woman once said, 'Life is what happens to you when you're busy being *totally humiliated*'. Or at least she would have done if she'd been me. If my life were a colour, it'd be *blush pink*.

**Most likely to say:** 'Come on ground - swallow me up already!'

**Least likely to say:** ' I just can't imagine life without my little brother.'

**Weak spots:** Are you kidding? OK, in no particular order: Strawberry ice cream, Ethan Craft, Ronny, Detention, Angel Lieberman, Mr Pettus' breath, cheerleaders, little brothers, unicorn sweaters, rice pudding, field trips, confrontation…and conversations about my hormones.

**Best moment:** Finally getting up the courage to ask Ethan out on a date … attagirl Lizzie, shoot for the moon!

**Worst Moment:** Ethan telling me he thinks 'we should just be friends'.

He's gone all of his life without doing it … but *now* he starts thinking??!

**Could surprise you by:** Anything - hey, the sky's the limit!

**Survival strategy:** Who me? I'm a pussycat. Everyone knows that!

# The Boys

**Name:** David Gordon

**A.K.A.:** Gordo. The Gordmeister. Gordzilla (NB. Last two only ever used by himself. *Once.*)

**Biog:** Gordo's not exactly cool, but he's not a geek either. He knows loads of stuff, and he truly moves to the beat of a different drummer.

**Most likely to say:** 'I'm engrossed in this great book: *The Structural Engineering of Model Bridges*.'

**Least likely to say:** 'I have *no* opinion on that subject.'

**Weak spots:** Monster Truck rallies. And he gets kinda weird about me dating guys … not sure why …

**Best moment:** For one tiny, beautiful moment, Gordo was the *swinginest* cat in the joint when Swing Music got big at Hillridge. He even gave Ethan tips on how to be cool. He had it *all*.

**Worst moment:** Swimming around in a sea of rice pudding. No more Mexican quiz shows for him!

> Like, bleurgh!

**Could surprise you by:** Telling you what you *need* to know … or *possibly* just something about Scandinavian leather industry import taxes. It's a bit of a lottery, to be honest.

**Survival strategy:** Like fertiliser, Gordo's wisdom is most useful spread thinly, but pretty bad when it's in a *great big heap* in front of you.

**Name:** Ethan Kraft

**A.K.A.:** Captain Wonderful / My Heart's Desire / Mr Hottie

**Biog:** Ethan is *totally* hot. He's the hottest guy in the school. He's so hot he has to wear asbestos pants…but, well, how to put this? It's a good thing he's pretty.

**Most likely to say:** 'I got stuck in a revolving door yesterday. There was, like, no exit!'

**Least likely to say:** 'Let's go to the library!'

**Weak spots:** Kate Sanders and her Cheerleading Bimbos. Hair gel adverts. And words of more than one *syll-a-ble*.

**Best moment:** Asking me out on a date once! A date! Me! And Ethan! Me and Ethan! Did I mention he asked me out?

I did, right? I did mention that, didn't I?

**Worst moment:** Any math test. Cute he can do, math he cannot do.

**Could surprise you by:** Announcing that some people are better off as friends… like *us*… ARGH!

**Survival strategy:** Ethan's like a cloud – beautiful to look at…just not very *substantial* is all.

**Name:** Tudgeman

**A.K.A.:** The Tudge. El Tudge.

**Biog:** You know when something terrible happens, and witnesses say 'But he was such a normal looking guy'? Nobody would say that about Tudgeman.

**Most likely to say:** 'All right – broccoli!'

**Least likely to say:** 'I'm sorry I can't attend your soiree, I'll be in the Hamptons that weekend.'

**Weak spots:** Actually, *nothing*. Popularity, wearing the right clothes, a regular *hygiene* routine – he couldn't care less!

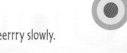

But if he lost his ten-sided dice he'd freak!

**Could surprise you by:** Showing you it's OK to be *yourself* – even if you're really weird …

**Best moment:** Dumping a whole bowl of punch over Kate. Dumping a whole bowl of punch over Kate. (I know I said it twice – I just like hearing it!)

**Worst Moment:** Eating worms for votes on Election Day. Yuck! On the other hand, he won!

**Survival strategy:** Smile nicely, and back away veeeerrry slowly.

# Friendship Quiz

We all need friends ... *especially* at school – it's a jungle out there!

I'm *really* lucky that Gordo and Miranda have got my back – they're the best! But not everyone's as lucky as me. In fact, some people's 'friends' are downright *uncool* ...like when Kate hurt her shoulder last semester, and what did her *so-called bestie*, Claire, do? Totally dissed her, that's what, and *then* got her canned from the cheerleading team!

So how can you tell if your friends are pals or piranhas?

**1** All your friends have started wearing really cute glitter tops to class. You really want one, but you can't afford it. What do your friends do?

**a)** Nothing. They say you look totally cool whatever you're wearing!

**b)** Chip in to buy you the top. Helping a friend look good = *priceless*!

**c)** Say 'Oh, are you still wearing *that*? *So* last season.'

**2** The hunkiest guy in the school – who everyone is crushing on – has just asked *you* out on a date. What do your friends say?

**a)** *Go girl!!* Let's get you set for the date!

**b)** Hey, that's really cool… I *guess*.

**c)** Wow! He picked *you*? Go figure!

**3** The big school dance is tomorrow. You've been looking forward to it all year, but you're sick with the flu! *Aaargh!* What do your friends do?

**a)** Ditch the dance, come over to your house and rent some videos!

**b)** Email you pix of the dance the following day, and tell you it was no fun without you.

**c)** Ask if they can borrow your coolest top... 'since you won't be needing it'.

**4** Your teacher thinks you've been cheating in a test. Only thing is, it was your *friend* who was cheating – you're innocent! What does your friend do?

**a)** Comes clean immediately – she can't let you take the fall!

**b)** Pleads with the teacher on your behalf. After all, she's sure you *'won't do it again...'*

**c)** Promises she'll visit you in *prison*.

**5** You've gotten friendly with the new kid. She's really nice, but a bit goofy. You introduce her to your friends – what do they say?

**a)** 'Hi there! Welcome to the neighbourhood. Wanna get some lunch with us?'

**b)** 'Hey, see you around, I guess.'

**c)** 'Eww, new kid!'

**6** You didn't make it on the cheerleading team, but all your friends *did*. What do they say?

**a)** Never mind, there's always the next tryouts!

**b)** Hey, you could always be our water-girl.

**c)** Gimme an L! O! S! E! R! And *whattya got…?!*

# Scoring:

## Mostly 'a's: Friends forever!

Don't let 'em get away. These are the kinds of friends that'll stay with you through *thick or thin*! They sound almost as cool as Miranda and Gordo. Definitely keepers!

## Mostly 'b's: Average buddies

Hmm, not bad, they've certainly got your best interests at heart. But they could try harder. Give 'em another chance…

## Mostly 'c's: Lower than the lowest

I've got a newsflash for you – these buddies are trouble! Are they there for you, or are you just there for them? Better have a rethink, before they freeze you out!

While you figure which one of *your* friends came out best, here's my little tribute to the best friend a girl could ever have…

# Reasons Why Miranda Rocks

Having a bestie at school is a sure-fire way to survival. You just can't make the journey alone! And I'm pretty lucky to have Miranda at my side, because…

- She stands up to Kate…even if I don't.

- She always listens to my problems…and even comes up with good advice.

- She can listen to Mr Pettus for *way* longer than I can before falling asleep.

- She doesn't care if she can't act – but she sure can sing!

- I've always got a lunch buddy to sit with.

- Between us, we can just about work out what Mr Dig is talking about. *Kind of*.

So that's why *my* best friend rocks… what about *yours*?

# My best friend rocks because...

# But Does He Really Like Me?

Calculus…world peace…the meaning of life – all *really* easy to sort out compared to the BIG question…'Does he really *like* me?'

Hey, you could always just try *talking* to him. (Just kidding. Like who's gonna do *that*?!!) Believe me, I've considered every method around to find out if Ethan likes me, and here are some you really *don't* want to use…

## Magic 8 Ball

If you don't like the answer it gives you, you can always try again. And again, and again, and *again* ... Let's face it, you could be shaking it all night!

## Telepathy

Useless. If this worked, I'd have crushed Matt's mind *like a soda can* by now. Don't even bother.

OK, concentrate ...
Ethan? Can you hear me,
Eeethannnnn?
Goooo out with
Liiizziiieee...

## Getting your mom to call his mom

Pretty good if you want to spontaneously combust from *sheer embarrassment*. Hey, make sure your mom mentions that you're 'simply adorable' for the kicker.

## Asking the kids at school what he thinks of you

I suppose sky-writing could be a *quicker* way of letting him know you're crushing on him, but this is *way* cheaper.

## Passing him a note in class

*So* second grade! Do you like me? Check one – Yes, No or Maybe.

# How To Be Popular

## Part I

❀ Be a cheerleader. Duh!

❀ Have a house with a pool, or failing that a *really* big TV.

❀ Have all the brains sucked out of your head with a *gigantic straw*.

**Footnote: Sub-human mutant brothers are a *definite* no-no.**

# She's All That... Right?

Sometimes it seems that being popular in school is the most important thing in the world. But is it really all that? I've been popular a few times...

Sure, like for ten *milli*seconds.

And there's always a downside. Like when I was a supermodel, everyone treated me differently. So let's take a look at reasons you might wanna be 'popular'...you might be surprised at what it really means...

# People like you more – right?

Yeah, maybe, but it's hard work being popular – you have to know a *lot* of people just a *little*.

Hey, it's tough being that shallow!

Popularity means that a lot of people know you, but it doesn't mean that they're your *friends*. I mean, I'm sure Claire doesn't even know what Kate's middle name is! But I know everything about *my* friends, even Gordo's dorky middle name (*Zephyr*. Sshh). Plus everyone likes to see the popular kids brought down a notch. Remember those creepy *Day of the Dead* Halloween skeletons, Kate? Quick! Rub some more chocolate cake in your hair to get rid of them!

# Popular people have more fun

Well, maybe, but Claire sure does spend a lot of her time organising *parties* and stuff. I mean, maybe she has fun bossing people around, but having a rep to keep up has gotta be pretty tiring. Tudgeman's got *no* human friends (I'm not counting DwarfLord Club...) but he has more fun with his *rotisserie baseball* and *amphibious skeletons* than Kate ever has queening it around school, I'll bet. Sometimes I think popularity's just a big act – a big, glamorous, fun act, that's all!

# Popular people are happy

This is so not true. Have you ever seen piranhas on the Animal Channel? Those guys are nothing compared to how popular people behave if they see someone wearing the wrong *sweater*...

> Look, for the last time it was a *present from Gammy*!

And if there's nothing to be witchy about...*they'll turn on each other*. Remember when Claire got Kate bumped from the cheerleading team, and she had to go to <gulp> the *dork hall*?

Ethan's pretty happy...but then Ethan would be happy if you gave him some *crayons* and a *pad*, so maybe he doesn't count.

## So in conclusion...

Worried about your *looks*? Worried about your *image*? Worried about your *clothes*? Worried about your *rep*? Sounds like a whole heap of worrying. Not worth it!

# How To Be Popular
## Part II

- ✿ Don't try too hard. Popular people are like dogs...they can *smell fear*.

- ✿ Start being so *un*popular and *un*cool that you actually start *coming out the other side*. (Sometimes known as the Gordo manoeuvre!)

# How to Survive...
# Popular Kids

## Cheerleaders & Jocks

Jumping around, running fast, and flunking math – you can see why these guys are our *natural superiors*...

So what makes these high school 'royals' tick? Check it out...

**Where they hang out:** The cafeteria, at sports games, in the hallway... anywhere people can see them and adore them!

**What to say to them:** Nothing. Don't speak to them unless they speak to you – you'll only regret it!

**What not to say to them:** 'Aren't you only popular because you stuff your bra with *tissue* paper? Hey, try Aisle Thirteen at the supermarket, there's *loads* of Kleenex there!'

**Their idea of a fun night:** The same as yours – only *you're* not invited!

**Popularity rating:** 10/10. (Just don't ask them what that'd be as a percentage...)

# Fashion Kids

They *look* right, they *act* right – and they won't do anything unless they've seen it in a magazine.

**Where they hang out:** In small elite groups in the school yard.

**What to say to them:** 'Hey, check out my new sneakers/top/organiser. You can only get them in *New York*.'

**What not to say to them:** 'Nice top. Betty's Bargains?'

**Their idea of a fun night:** Checking out the new arrivals at the mall…so they can boast about them in class the next day.

**Popularity rating:** 8/10. (But only because the number eight is fashionable this year.)

# Are You Truly Cool At School?

Being popular at school might *seem* important… but you sure have to hang out with some queen bees! I'm not sure it's worth it. It's better to take a leaf out of Gordo's book – just be yourself.

**Be more like *Gordo*? You crazy lady!**

Hey, bear with me… he does what he likes, has fun with his friends, and doesn't care what other people think. That's pretty cool, and way better than being a so-called 'popular' kid. So do you wanna just be popular, or *truly cool*? Answer these questions to find out.

**1** There's a 'Girls Invite Boys' Dance at school, but you'd rather stay in and catch a movie. What do you do?

**a)** Go anyway – your friends would never forgive you!

**b)** Watch that movie – your friends can make the popcorn!

**2** Would you rather…

**a)** Have everyone at school know who you are?

**b)** Really know who your friends are?

**3** You're having a bad hair day. Do you…

**a)** Pretend you're sick, so you can't go to school?

**b)** Go anyway, wearing your favourite hat to cover up the disaster?

**4** Your popular school friends catch you in front of… the *museum*! What do you say?

**a)** Oh, hi guys, just going in to use the restroom. What *is* this place anyway?

**b)** Have you seen the *Rusty Old Coin Collection* here? It rocks!

**Mostly 'b's** You don't care what other people think at school because you're *truly cool*!

**Mostly 'a's** Watch out, you *could* end up like Kate!

# How To Survive...
# Double E's

Doesn't matter where you go to school,
*every* place has got them. They love playing
DwarfLord, solving word puzzles and
wearing pocket protectors. Whether you
call them geeks or dweebs, Double E's are
everywhere. But how can you tell them
apart? Take a look at my handy guide!

# Mathletes

Wow, where to start? Algebra – they love it! Quadratic Equations – you betcha! Calculus – all *over* it! These guys just can't get enough.

Hey, wasn't Dad a Mathlete? Figures!

**Where they hang out:** The math classroom, and the library (checking out the Dewey Decimal system…)

**What to say to them:** 'How about those *integers*, hey?'

**What not to say to them:** 'I just heard the Supreme Court made a new ruling, and now $\pi$ is *just 3*.' (They'll explode!)

**Their idea of a fun night:** Having some friends over for a sleepover, making some popcorn, and counting to a million.

**Double E Rating:** 10/10. No, wait – $10^{10}$

# Chess Clubbers

Sitting still. Planning. Thinking things through *real slow*. Chess has it all! And these guys love *anything* to do with chess.

**Where they hang out:** Nice quiet rooms, or anywhere with a black & white tiled floor.

**What to say to them:** 'Chess is the sport of kings!'

**What not to say to them:** 'Isn't this just like checkers, only *more* dull?'

**Their idea of a fun night:** Reading transcripts of historic chess matches.

*Kasparov: QKn4*

*Deep Blue: KnC3*

*Kasparov: CKn4*

Hey, don't spoil the ending for me!

**Double E Rating:** 8/10.

# The Orchestra (A.K.A. The Dorkestra)

Keeping time... obeying orders... endlessly talking about *sousaphones*... what's *not* cool about the orchestra?!

On the other hand... having a talent other than rhythmic gymnastics would be nice!

**Where they hang out:** The school hall.

**What to say to them:** 'You guys will never guess how much gunk I collected in my *spit valve* last practise!'

**What not to say to them:** 'Don't you guys ever get tired of playing the theme song from *Star Wars*?'

**Their idea of a fun night:** Listening to their favourite album, *Greatest Hits of the Solo Bassoon*.

**Double E Rating:** 7/8 (time).

# School of Cool: Where Do You Fit in?

Ever wondered where you are in the scheme of things? Take a look at this useful chart I've created to help you work out where you are in the popularity stakes. Check off where you belong!

A chart? A *useful* chart? Mr Pettus, watch out!

O **CHEERLEADERS:** Top of the tree. Junior high royalty.

**Off with their heads!**

O **POPULAR CROWD:** Still very popular, and wouldn't talk to, say, *me*.

O **THEATRE CLUB:** Lights! Camera! Snobbery!

O **GLEE CLUB:** Miranda tried out for these guys, so I guess they can't be *too* popular. (Sorry!)

O **LIZZIE & MIRANDA:** Kinda halfway up the popularity slope. Hey, join us!

O **GORDO:** A league of his own, and that's the way he likes it.

O **THE AV CLUB:** Microphones! Magnetic Tape! Vertical Hold! What *doesn't* the AV club have to offer?

**Uh, social credibility?**

O **MATHLETES:** Good at math, not good at 'cool'.

O **THE MARCHING BAND:** Making jokes about flutes really doesn't cut it. Trust me on this.

O **SCIENCE CLUB:** Most people have never even *seen* a Science Clubber…but they're out there somewhere.

O **TUDGEMAN:** He's here, he's weird – get *used* to it!

# Horrible Scenarios Too Horrible To Think About

**Number One: Your little bro is at the same school as you.**

This can go one of two ways. Either it's really cool to have a sib at your school, you really enjoy seeing them every day, and they don't embarrass you at all…

And then there's what *actually* happens. Most of the time you'd rather listen to Mr Pettus sing *The Periodic Table Song* than speak to your kid brother at school. (And Mr Pettus' singing is something which is banned in all states. Look it up!)

**For:** OK, so maybe having a younger sib at school isn't *all* bad. You'll always have someone there to talk to, or look after, and you can pass on your excellent School Survival Tips!

**Against:** If your bro is anything like *mine* …

…then you don't want him in the same school. Or on the same *planet*.

Mars? Mmm, I dunno, it's kinda near. *Jupiter's* nice this time of year though!

**The worst that could happen:** He could become more popular than you, make all the kids at your school *love* him, and then hang with your favourite hottie and freeze you out.

**What to do:** *Hello?* Is that emergency services?

# The Teachers

**Name:** Mr Dig

**A.K.A.:** Hey, does he even *have* a first name? Does 'Mister' count?

**Biog:** Our substitute teacher – he substitutes stuff he makes up for real lessons. Fun though!

**Most likely to say:** 'OK – I want you to deliver your book report, but through the medium of *contemporary dance*.'

**Least likely to say:** 'Let's concentrate on the textbook. Then we'll have a test.'

**Weak spots:** Getting off the point. Last week we ended up going through the *entire* American Revolution…in *math* class.

**Best moment:** Getting Miranda, Gordo and me through the Fact-a-thlon…*and* we avoided going to Florida! Kate's still peeling from the sunburn!

> That sounds dangerously like *learning*, McGuire.

**Worst moment:** Wiping out in front of everybody on his scooter. But he just got up and dusted himself off!

**Could surprise you by:** Giving you the *real deal* on life. Mr Dig lets you tackle problems your own way.

**Survival strategy:** Just hang on and enjoy the ride!

**Name:** Mr Pettus

**A.K.A.:** Mr Dweebus (Kate's idea, by the way)

**Biog:** Mr Pettus is half science geek and half nerd. But for a guy who sets himself on fire so frequently, he's pretty cool.

**Most likely to say:** '$H_2SO_4$'

**Least likely to say:** 'Aw, it's *only* chemistry...'

**Weak spots:** 'The fascinating beauty of the periodic table.' Hey, *he* said it!

**Best moment:** When mom took the rap for TP-ing the boys' tent on the field trip. Shoulda seen his face!

**Worst moment:** Threatening to make me eat rat on a field trip has to be pretty far up the list! He got far too *Survivor* on that trip, let me tell you!

The first three rows, you *will* lose your eyebrows.

**Could surprise you by:** Spontaneously combusting before your very eyes. When Mr Pettus teaches you about safety in the lab, you better stand by with the fire extinguisher.

**Survival strategy:** Keep your wits about you and a fire extinguisher nearby.

# Code Blue!
# Assignment Failure!

It happens to the best of us – you get to class, and suddenly you remember you were supposed to hand in your assignment today!

Enterprise?
One to beam
aboard… *quick*!

So what do you do? Do you try and bluff your way out? Or should you just take the rap? There are several ways forward… up to you to choose!

# 1. Get out of class – quick

Remember this rule about getting out of class – the wilder the reason, the quicker you get out…but the more dangerous it becomes! If you say you've got a headache, you might not get out of class at all…but if you say you've just remembered you have to go have *experimental brain surgery* today, it'll either get you out quick, or get you rushed to the ER!

## Good ways to get out of class:

* Faking a fainting fit (you might not have to fake it if it's a really big assignment!)

* Speaking in tongues.

* Pretending you just saw a *giant bird* kidnap Coach Kelly outside. (NB. Will only work once.)

# 2. Think of an excuse

I'm *terrible* at excuses – I crack quicker than Kate's foundation on a hot day. On the other hand, my miserable excuse for a *brother* is a world-class excuse-maker. He doesn't get many assignments at his school, but he hands them in late on *general principle*.

## Matt's 'Top Ten Reasons Why My Assignment's Late'

❀ I realised no one would be able to comprehend its genius.

❀ I did hand it in…*metaphorically* speaking.

❀ It caught on fire. Then a dog ate it. Then the dog caught on fire.

❀ The aliens told me not to hand it in.

❀ It fell through a time-warp…so I actually handed it in last year.

❀ I've done the assignment in Morse Code.
Here goes >ahem< *bee-deep-bee-dip-dip-dee-dip-dip-dee-dee*…

❀ There *was* no assignment. And these *aren't* the droids you're looking for.

❀ Lizzie used the paper to write love-notes on.

❀ I'm afraid I can't hand in the paper on religious grounds.

❀ I thought you said 17 June 2005.

# 3. Grovel pathetically

There's only one thing teachers like more than straight, truthful apologising... and that's pathetic grovelling! Only use as a last resort, because it could bring your cool rating *way* down. For extreme emergencies, here's one I prepared for you earlier:

'Uh, about that, Mr Coopersmith, I, er, what I mean to say is, my you're looking so well today Mr Coopersmith... yes, the assignment, well, uh, I forgot to, er, is that new cologne Mr Coopersmith? Uh, yes well, umm, so sorry Mr Coopersmith.'

**Guess which one I usually go for!**

# Untrue School Facts

## Part I

* School is Latin for 'arena of humiliation'.

* School was invented by Abraham Lincoln in 1860 as a way to use up the nation's chalk mountain.

* Cafeteria food is twenty percent sawdust

Yeah, it's actually fifty percent!

# How To Survive... Class!

## English Class

Great if you're a descendant of Shakespeare, but pretty lame if you're not. The best that can happen to you in English class is being asked to read out a part in a play with some *totally* cute guy as your love interest.

But let's face it, that doesn't happen very often, and when you're not trying to write a book report on a book you haven't actually read, you're having to learn about some book that was written *a hundred years ago*.

It's in the past, just let it *go*!

My advice is to keep your head down, learn your verbs, and get ready to play Juliet to Ethan's Romeo!

# Music Class

As Shakespeare once said: 'If music be the food of love… then Ethan's a *symphony*!' Music is pretty cool, but don't get it confused with the Marching Band, which is *not so* cool. In class you get to listen to a lot of music, which can be fun – even if sometimes that music is Gordo's *African Throat Singers'* CD. And if your music teacher's voice is as bad as mine then you can say *goodbye* to a peaceful period.

> Yowza!
> Can you hear that?
> Is there a *cat*
> trapped in a well
> somewhere?

## Social Studies

This class totally rocks. Why? Well, where else could
Miranda get married to Ethan, or Gordo find out that he's
going to be a blackjack dealer, or I find out I should train
to be a cosmetologist? Pretty much *anything* can happen
in Social Studies…

Fingers crossed
for Kate getting
eaten by a *dinosaur*
then.

…but you need to pick and choose. Learning about who
you'll be when you grow up is pretty cool, but learning
about the judicial system is strictly for the nerds. Hey, but
any lesson that can end up with Kate getting three gallons
of cherry punch tipped over her big hair has gotta have
something going for it!

# Dig for Victory?

Sometimes you actually *learn* stuff in school – I'm not making this up! I mean, most of the time you're supposed to be learning something *else*, but when Mr Dig is your teacher, you generally end up better informed…

❁ Like when Miranda, Gordo and me were studying for the *Fact-a-thlon* – Mr Dig helped us study in a way that was exciting, not just lame facts. We didn't *win*… but we sure had fun learning.

❁ Or like when I became a supermodel – Mr Dig told me I should go for it, but maybe he really knew I wouldn't like it in the end… and so he just let me find out for myself.

❁ Or like on the scavenger hunt. I truly realised that winning wasn't the most important thing… not if it hurt my friends.

Hey – I guess you *can* learn stuff at school… you've just gotta look for the hidden lessons. They're everywhere. Oh, except algebra – there's *nothing* to learn there, believe me.

Maybe Mr Dig isn't as flaky as he makes out. Maybe some teachers are actually interested in helping you learn stuff… in an exciting way. *Maybe* he's a man with a plan.

Or maybe he's just *really* out there. Who knows?!

# Lizzie's Study Tips

## Part I

No one likes to do it, but sometimes it's gotta be done.

What?
It's family portrait
time *again*?

I'm talking about studying. Read my ideas on how to get the learning done faster so you can get back to thinking about Justin Timberlake…

## 1. Find a quiet place

If you can't hear, you can't *study* – so it's best to find a quiet place where you can settle down to work. If you're anywhere near Matt's *Mile of Death* Skateboard Track, or Miranda *bringing the house down* in Drama Class, or Tudgeman with his *Star Wars* impressions…

…then it's pretty much a bust. If you're at school, why not try the library? It's real quiet, has tons of books… and *nobody goes there – ever.*

## 2. Cut out distractions

Even if your study place is a real *quiet* place –
like the library, or the *Larry Tudgeman
Appreciation Society* – you can still distract
yourself. Definite no-no's include: playing music,
thinking about Ethan Craft, trying to work out
what Gordo was talking about earlier, wondering
what Ethan Craft is doing *right now*, pondering
why paperboys make *really bad boyfriends*,
weighing up the pros of learning *Spanish* if
you're going on a Mexican game show,
wondering whether Ethan Craft is thinking about
*you* right now, or trying to figure why Brooke
would want to go on a date with Gordo. Any of
that is a bad distraction.

## 3. Study with a buddy

Studying with a pal is a good way to learn together. You can test each other, help each other, and it doesn't seem so scary if you've got lots to do. Friends can make studying just about bearable. (But hey, Mr Pettus, it's never gonna be 'the most rewarding thing you'll ever do'. Nice try.)

**You've gotta choose your buddy carefully... it's a minefield out there!**

- *Not* someone you're secretly crushing on – studying and crushes don't mix. It'll end up either a lousy study session…or a *really* lame date.

- *Not* someone you *can't understand* half the time – like a certain Mr Gordon.

- *Not* someone you have too much fun with – you can make it interesting, but it's not a sleepover party!

- *Not* your little brother: too young to help – not old enough for the *army*. Avoid.

- *Not* someone who's going to go off to *summer* camp and come back with a *small* bra and a *big* 'tude and then start *dissing* you for no *reason*.

- Not dad's cousin ReRe – because he lives in Minneapolis. What a *weird* suggestion…

# Coping With Being...
# An F Student

**Omigod! That's *it*! Stick a fork in me – I'm *done*! These are some of the things you might be thinking if you get an F. But it's *not* the end of the world!**

Sometimes, getting an F can be a good thing... it can make you want to do better next time, or highlight that there's something you don't understand about the subject. Look at it as a warning signal, do something about it, and move on. And if *that* doesn't cheer you up, just think about what good company you'll be in... you could study with Ethan!

# Coping With Being...
# An A Student

What? Am I for *real*? There are problems with being an A student? Gimme a *break*! Well, yeah – there can be! Just because you get straight 'A's (like Gordo) doesn't mean your life's perfect. And it's not a guarantee that you'll become popular around school either (like Gordo).

Good grades are important, but you don't want to wreck your life getting them. So if you feel your life is getting swamped by the pressure of grades, and you're getting overwhelmed, why not talk to a good friend about it? Like Gordo!

# Lizzie's Study Tips

## Part II

### Set goals for yourself

Studying can be tough - especially if you have to research the national dish of Latvia at short notice…

Latvia? Didn't he win *Wimbledon* last year?

…but you can break up the study time by setting yourself goals. Try to get something finished before rewarding yourself with a break, or getting a snack - stuff to look forward to, like:

- ❀ having a soda
- ❀ taking a walk around the house
- ❀ marrying Ethan Craft
- ❀ transporting your kid brother to the Phantom Zone
- ❀ having a number one hit
- ❀ meeting Justin Timberlake
- ❀ eating a tuna melt

# Instant Genius!

OK, so you need to impress a teacher – quick! What do you say? No problem – Lizzie's on the case. Throw these into your class conversation and you'll sound like Einstein. Just make sure you get the timing right, that's all!

**English:** 'This passage has a very *Joycean* feel to it, Mr Coopersmith.'

Err, yeah, that's what I think, too.

**Math:** 'Yes, but that solution can only work in non-*Euclidean* mathematics, of course...'

And if anyone asks you what *that* means... run!

**History:** 'I'm not sure studying by period helps – I like to take a more *holistic* approach to history.'

Holistic... is that the study of *holes*?

**Gym:** 'Can I do *more* laps, Coach Kelly?'

*Dumb* – but it'll impress 'em...

# Places Not To Study

## The bowling alley

Too crowded, too stinky…plus you might get distracted by the sound of one of your friends getting a bowling ball cut off their *hand*. Avoid.

## Your local coffee shop (like the 'Bean)

This sounds like a good idea, but then it's…*just a cappuccino please*…and then…*and a muffin*…plus a little…*oh hey! Is that Ethan talking to Vic over there?* Way too distracting!

## The cafeteria

You might get some work done here, but you also might get real queasy from the smell of *cafeteria cheese*.

# Untrue School Facts

## Part II

- You spend over eight million hours in school during your lifetime.

- Hall monitors are worthy of your respect.

- Gym teachers are well-rounded individuals with lots of friends.

# The Day Of Reckoning

### A.K.A. Parent-Teacher Conference Night!

I study hard, I have Gordo help me with the difficult stuff, and I hand my assignments in on time. Well, *almost* always on time. But I never know what the verdict will be on Parent-Teacher night.

Whether it's a good report, or a bad one, you should always be prepared. So take a look at my survival guide to Parent-Teacher reports.

# If your report is bad...

❊ Deny everything your teachers said about you. Keep denying it until you're twenty-one and can leave home.

❊ Say "D's are the new 'A's – you are *so last year*, Mom!'

❊ Stare at your folks *real hard* and chant: 'You are veerrry happy with my report. Veeeerrry happy...'

❊ Tell your folks the school is built on top of a *giant underground magnet*, and it wiped out your memory.

❊ Say 'It's because of all the *lead* in the cafeteria lasagne.'

❊ Say 'I know I got bad grades – but I've been learning to do *this*!' Then start dancing like a crazy person.

# If your report is good...

❊ Say 'A good report is its own reward... but about that *car*...'

❊ There will never be a better time to talk about getting your belly button pierced, for example.

❊ Suggest that it's time for your little brother to go to Military Academy. Leave a brochure for your folks to read.

❊ Suggest you finish with school 'on a high note' and start working for *Teen Scene* Magazine as a model.

# Cheater Cheater Pencil Eater!

OK, let's get *serious* here for a second. At some point in your school life, you're gonna get the opportunity to cheat on a test, or maybe help someone else cheat. So you wanna hear my survival tip for this scenario? Listen up real good, cause I don't want you to miss this.

Why? Here's why – it's a lose-lose situation! You either get caught or you get away with it, and neither's good. The only time I cheated on a test, I helped Angel *'Doberman'* Lieberman out…and I got busted! I got sent to detention too, and had to lie to my mom about where I was. For a while I was so off base I even *hung out* with Angel Lieberman!

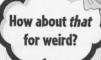

**How about *that* for weird?**

And that's just the *best* result! Because even if you're not caught, you start to feel guilty (like when the Principal's statue got busted and the Spring Fling was cancelled... and I didn't even *do* it!). Pretty soon you're gonna start thinking about smuggling yourself to Canada and starting your life over as a *lumberjack*.

Believe me – it's not worth it. So next time you get the chance, just think: what's worse... getting a C in the test, or living in a *log cabin* for the rest of your life?

Just you and the wood lice.

# Take A Chill Pill!

Studying can be tough – especially when you've got two assignments to hand in, and you know there's a pop quiz happening in the afternoon. But getting stressed is only gonna make things worse.

## Try to unwind by:

### Breathing deeply

Sounds lame, but it really can help, and you can do it anywhere. More air to your brain helps you think better and stay chilled.

### Taking a walk

Just moving around helps, and can take your mind off your worries. Just don't walk straight out of school!

### Having something to look forward to

Think 'OK, so I've got that quiz, but this evening me and my buds will rent a movie.' Give yourself a cool goal to reach for!

# Faking It

Now this is something I never do, but there are times when you *just can't* go to school. Whether you're wearing a unicorn sweater, or have a giant zit on the end of your nose...

Pulling a sickie rocks! Wuhoo!

... faking an illness is the only way to go. Now personally I'm not a good faker, but I am related to one of the fakiest kids there is. Check out the stuff I've copied from Matt's *Notebook of Doom* ...

# Matt McGuire's Guide To Faking It:

## ① Seeing Spots

### You will need:

1 x felt tip pen
1 x short-sighted mom

### Method:

Apply the felt tip pen to your face creating a dotted effect (don't forget your eyelids!). Then groan and say you've got any one of the following:

- Chicken pox
- Measles
- A terrible rash

### Helpful tip:

Don't overdo it and claim you have *small*pox. They will take you away in a plastic bag and burn all your stuff.

### Success rating:

5/10. But it does depend on how thick your mom's glasses are…

## (2) Gimme Fever

### You will need:

1 x lamp with working lightbulb
1 x thermometer

### Method:

Tell your mom you have a headache and a terrible temperature (remember, no one can *check* for headaches!). When her back's turned, take the thermometer out of your mouth and hold it against the lightbulb* just for a split second. Instant high reading!

### Helpful tip:

Don't overdo it and leave it there for five minutes. No one will believe a fever of 250° – you are not a human torch.

### Success Rating:

It's 100 watts of pure brilliance!

*make sure it's *on* first!

## ③ The Old Switcheroo

### You will need:

1 x the acting skills of Robert De Niro

### Method:

In the morning, ask your mom for a ride to school, because 'I feel really weird and headachey today but I *don't want to miss school*'. Everytime she asks if you're OK, say that you're completely fine, then sigh heavily and blink lots. Don't forget – you *want* to go to school …

### Helpful tip:

Don't overdo it and start saying stuff that no one would ever believe, like 'I've just *gotta* get to school and take that algebra test … I've just *gotta!*'

### Success Rating:

Hmm, could go either way – either a bust from the get go, or a sure-fire cinch. Nothing in between.

# How Not To Phone In Sick

Of course, I'd never normally do this, but if it were an *extreme* emergency, like Matt dyeing my hair blue, I might have to consider it.

**You:** 'Hello there, good morning. I'm afraid Lizzie McGuire won't be in school today, she's sick.'

**Teacher:** 'Oh, I'm sorry to hear that ... and who is this speaking, please?'

**You:** 'Umm, this is my father speaking.'

**You:** 'Hello there, this is the President of the United States calling. Just to let you know, Lizzie McGuire is on a top secret mission for me and won't be in school today.'

**Teacher:** 'Oh *really* – what's your middle name, Mr President?'

**You:** 'Err, I don't *know*. Goodbye! Vote Republican!'

# Dodgeball:
## Fun Game Or Painful Ordeal Of Terror?

Dodgeball should be banned under international law. Until it is, here's some information that might help you get out alive:

- Dodgeball was invented during WW2 as a way of making *prisoners confess*.

- The greatest number of simultaneous dodgeball hits was six – sustained by one Larry Tudgeman of Hillridge Junior High, last year. Doctors say he may *still* not be right in the head.

- If you rearrange the letters in 'dodgeball' you get – 'dead ball'. Well, *almost*.

- Coach Kelly is wanted in over seventeen states for *dodgeball related crimes*.

- The only way to survive a dodgeball game intact… is *not to play*.

# Field Day

Now I quite like *some* sports – I'm pretty cool at rhythmic gymnastics actually! But there are quite a few sports I *don't* like (pretty much anything suggested by Coach Kelly). One big area you've gotta watch out for is Field Day. Why? Let me spell it out:

- ❈ lots of competitive sports
- ❈ the *whole school* watching you
- ❈ …and *judging* you
- ❈ …and *mocking* you
- ❈ your mom and dad being there

**_Hel-lo_ – recipe for total humiliation! I'd rather ballroom dance with the Tudge again!**

My advice is to sign yourself up for stuff that won't embarrass you to death, like…

## Egg-and-Spoon Race

No pressure, no one takes it seriously, and no one cares if you look dumb!

(Because who _doesn't_ look dumb balancing an egg on a spoon…?)

## Triple Jump

So boring that no one will want to watch it. You're safe!

## Relay Race

Just make sure you're not on the last leg, and then no one will blame you even if you lose!

Or why not try my personal favourite: join the Field Day boosters! All you have to do is sit on the sidelines, cheer, and serve orange juice – no problem! And the great thing about being on the sidelines is that you can watch all the hotties getting hot & sweaty.

What's that? Ethan's in the swim race? HOLD THE PHONE!

# How to Survive...
# Field Trips

## What to do if... your mom comes along!

Wow! Tough spot... not only is your mom coming along, which is pretty embarrassing, but she'll also be kinda acting like a teacher – gets worse – *and* trying to 'talk to your little friends'. Total humiliation! Be warned, she may even try to 'talk the slang' with them.

Uh-oh,
I'm having flashbacks
to when Dad said he was
*The Real Sam Shady...*

## Survival tactic:

Relax! Getting uptight won't help, and the others might start to tease you if they see you're embarrassed. So what if your mom's there – she's pretty cool really!

# Field Trips To Museums

The Museum of Pop Music, The National Centre for Cute Boys, or the Royal Accessorising and Sleepover Museum… these are all places that your teacher *never* takes you to. No - instead say hello to fossils, coins, broken pots, rocks, charts and *really old bottles*.

Must… stay… awake…

## Survival tactic:

Every museum has a gift shop and a café - even the really lame ones! If you've got a worksheet to do, team up with friends to get it done quicker… then hit the café in search of cute guys!

## Survival no-no:

Don't buy stuff in the gift shop just cause you're there… hotties do not dig 'I went to the *Kalamazoo Museum of Cheese*!' T-shirts. Trust me.

# Field Trips To Fields

Ahh! The Great Outdoors!
Fresh Air!
Trees!
Flowers!

Bears!
Snakes!
Rain!

Believe me – you should *fake an illness* rather than go on a nature field trip, where the whole of nature is *against* you ... and that's *before* your teacher goes psycho and makes you eat *rat* for dinner. Well, almost ...

## Survival tactic:

Find shelter, and fast! First get those tents set up – so find some boys to do it (they've gotta be useful for *something*, right?). Once you're cosy in your sleeping bag, open up the snacks and start spinning those ghost stories. What, you *didn't* know this was an *Ancient Indian Burial Site* ...?
**Whoooo...whooooo!**

# Field Trips To The Theatre

Well, the theatre can be kinda fun, but it depends on what you're seeing. (NB. if the title is *Greasier* starring Miranda Sanchez...*run for the hills!*)

## Survival tactic:

Don't get too depressed if it turns out you're going to see a really old play, like Shakespeare or something – deep down, most of them are pretty interesting, with love stories, sword fights and even the odd joke!

**Hey, I'm not making this up – *Gordo* told me!**

So you *could* end up having fun after all. Just don't fall asleep when the lights go out!

## Survival no-no:

Don't throw rotten fruit at the actors. That stuff stains.

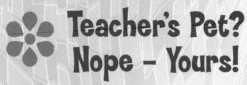

# Teacher's Pet?
# Nope – Yours!

Every school has a pet, and some are luckier than others. Some get to be taken home by a nice family, looked after, pampered, and sent back to school with a *smile* on their snout.

And some school pets get looked after by *Matt*. We *buried* his school's pet lizard… on the first day he looked after it.

I mean, how can you tell if it's alive or dead anyway?

As you can imagine, that earned him a *really* bad rep at his school. Survival moral here? *Don't look after school pets* – if they roll over on you, your *reputation* takes a dirt nap too.

If you're asked to pet-sit... watch out! Pets you certainly *don't* want to look after include:

- Stick insects – well, were you just listening to what I *said*?
- A hamster with an eating problem and a weak heart.
- Any type of poisonous toad.
- A dinosaur.
- A Black Mamba snake.
- An elephant which has just eaten a lot of bran.
- An electric eel (from the petting zoo).
- A mayfly (pretty likely it's not gonna last!).
- Any kind of animal that can get itself *lost*, wedged under the *floorboards*, into the *garden* or stuck in the *microwave*.

# The Cafeteria:

## A Nice Place To Visit, But Hold The Cheese!

The cafeteria is: a place to hang out; somewhere you might get to see how cute Ethan's looking; a place to avoid Kate; or just somewhere you can go and watch Tudgeman try to eat *three pounds of jelly*.

The cafeteria is not: somewhere you should eat. Right? Just in case you are, here's the 411 on what's good to eat, and what should hit the street...

# Good

## Apples

These are pretty safe. No cooking involved so not even Lunchlady Doris can get it wrong. But make sure you wash it first, just to be sure.

## Broccoli

Anything that's been boiled so much has gotta be clean. Right?

## Packaged Cookies

Protected from all the elements!

## Water

This is OK. If it's been boiled.

# Bad

## Hamburgers

Are you kidding me? Those things are made out of *mystery meat* – if you're lucky. Stick to your favourite burger place, like the excellent Digital Bean.

## Jelly

*Hell-lo* – were you listening earlier? Tugdeman's favourite food, and it's made from horses' *hooves*. Ew!

So, the cafeteria: come for the company, leave before you accidentally eat something.

# Cafeteria Etiquette

You think going to the cafeteria is *easy*? Think you can sit where you *want*, *talk* to who you want? Think again my friend! Take a look at my handy diagram to reveal the pitfalls of cafeteria choreography.

# Shall We Dance?

What is it with my friends and school dances? Either I can't go to the *Spring Fling* cause I'm taking the rap for Kate busting that statue of the principal...

**Hey you kids! Cut that out!**

...or Gordo gets turned down by Parker when he asks her to be his date because he's too short, or *I* ask Ethan to a dance...and he turns me down...*twice*!

School dances are bad news! You get all nervous about asking someone out – and even if they say 'yes' then you're nervous for the whole week beforehand. If you really wanna ask someone to go, here are a few tips:

- ❉ Remember, your date is probably just as nervous as you.

- ❉ Don't try too hard to impress them – just be yourself*.

- ❉ Don't drink the punch. It'll be horrible, and you'll get it on your outfit. Yuck.

- ❉ If Ethan Craft comes on to the dance floor – watch out for his *arms*. And *legs*…

- ❉ How *tall* you are doesn't matter – it's how much fun you are to be with! (Right, Gordo?)

- ❉ Even the popular kids are nervous at school dances – remember, they've got reps to defend!

* (NB. If you're Tudgeman, *don't* be yourself.)

# Eww, What Is That?

No matter what school you go to, every school has its own weird smell – one that doesn't smell quite like anything else on earth. Ever wondered what makes up that smell? Here's *my* guess:

- Cafeteria food.

- The sweet smell of success coming off the Popular Kids.

- Tudgeman's socks (when he *wears* socks).

- Ethan's cologne.

- The charred remains of Mr Pettus' lab coat.

- Mr Coopersmith's smouldering good looks.

- The stench of defeat from our basketball team.

- Monday morning blues.

# Lizzie McGuire, Survival Guru, Signing Out

So there you go – my crucial guide to surviving school! It's been real. And hey, it must be working so far because you're still reading! Keep this book with you at all times – you never know when you might need it. But if you only remember one thing, it should be this: if you've got good friends around you, and you know who you are, then you'll never go wrong.

Oh yeah, and Ethan's phone number. That'd help too!

So best wishes, best foot forward, and remember – no matter how embarrassed you might be at times, at least your pants never split showing the whole class you were wearing 'Tuesday' underwear (on a Wednesday).

Does amnesia come bottled?

If by any chance this book hasn't helped you survive your school, you can always get a transfer to Hillridge! Miranda, Gordo and I will look after you. (Just remember to duck when Kate comes round the corner!)

## Catch you later,

### Love,

# Lizzie